REY'S TRANSCONTINENTAL TALE: PANAMA TO THE UNITED STATES

Reinaldo A. Whyte

Dedication

*D*edicated *To The Three Most Extraordinary Women in My Life,*

In the enchanting symphony of my journey, I dedicate this book to you with a heart brimming with profound gratitude and boundless admiration. Each of you, in your own remarkable way, has imprinted indelible marks upon the canvas of my existence, igniting a fire within my soul that guides me through the darkest of nights and empowers me to embrace the brilliance of every dawn.

To my beloved mother, Rosa Whyte, you have been the anchor that steadies my course amid the tumultuous seas of life. Your unwavering love, and resilience, early in my life, has continued to be the rock upon which I lean when the storms threaten to overwhelm me. You gifted me the strength to forge ahead, even when the world conspired against my dreams.

Lolita Asper, my piano teacher and inspiration, you graced my life with the transformative power of music. Your tutelage not only honed my musical abilities but also

i

bestowed upon me a profound understanding of courage and authenticity. Early in my life, you encouraged me to embrace the passion that burns within, unshackled from the judgments of others, and this has liberated my spirit and infused my art with a depth of emotion that resonates far beyond mere notes on a page.

And to my dearest wife, Jenniffer Whyte, you are the luminous beacon that lights my way through the labyrinth of uncertainties. With your unwavering belief in me, even in moments when I doubt myself, you lift me to soaring heights. Your boundless love, unwavering support, and gentle hand that lifts me when I falter are the celestial forces that propel me onward, a constant reminder that we are an unyielding team, united by love and devotion.

This book bears witness to the tapestry of my life, woven with the threads of your love and influence. It is a testament to the profound impact each of you has had on the person I've become, and the dreams I dare to chase. Without you, my journey would be but an echo, a whisper in the winds of time. Your presence in my life colors every chapter with passion, authenticity, and boundless inspiration.

May these pages be a humble tribute to the love you've bestowed upon me—a love that has nurtured my soul, lifted my spirit, and given me the strength to weave the intricate patterns of my existence. As I offer this work to the world, it is you, my three muses, who dance within every word, every phrase, and every sentiment, breathing life into the tale I yearn to tell.

With all my love and devotion

Reinaldo A. Whyte

About The Author

Meet Reinaldo A. Whyte, an author whose journey from Panama City, Panama, to the United States, has shaped his debut story, Rey's Continental Tale.

Born in Panama City, Reinaldo grew up amidst seven siblings, discovering his love for storytelling amidst the dynamics of family life and extreme poverty. As a husband, father of five, concert musician, foster parent, and pastor, he balanced multiple roles while nurturing his writing passion.

As an English as a Second Language Teacher, Reinaldo's understanding of language enriches his storytelling, offering readers an immersive experience.

Rey's Continental Tale marks the beginning of Reinaldo A. Whyte's literary journey, promising captivating narratives that transcend borders and hearts. Stay tuned for more from this talented wordsmith.

Contents

Preface

In the vast tapestry of life, there are stories that weave across continents, bridging borders, cultures, and experiences. This is the tale of Rey, a brave boy whose journey begins in the picturesque landscapes of Panama and takes him on an unforgettable adventure to the United States. From the bustling streets of Rio Abajo to the unfamiliar cityscapes of America, Rey's story is one of resilience, curiosity, and growth.

"Rey's Transcontinental Tale: From Panama to the United States" invites readers on a heartfelt voyage through the eyes of a young boy, from fourth to sixth grade. Each chapter of this book represents a cherished fragment of his life, a collection of moments that shaped his world and left indelible marks on his heart.

The journey commences with "Happy Birthday to Me," where we meet a young Rey celebrating a special day amidst the vibrant colors of his Panamanian home. As the tale unfolds in "It Starts Here," readers witness the turning point in Rey's life—a moment that propels him towards a future he couldn't have imagined.

Accompanied by "Zultana and the Elementary School," we follow him as he ventures into the realm of education, forging new friendships and discovering the wonders of learning. As Rey adapts to his surroundings in "Getting Used to My Surroundings," we share his joys and challenges in navigating the beauty and complexities of Panama. We revel in his encounters with the country's diverse wildlife in "Encountering Panama's Wildlife" and savor the sweetness of life in "I Like Sugar."

In "The Church and the Nail," Rey's parents' faith becomes central in shaping his perspective. "Dreams Unmet" explores the poignant moments where his parents' aspirations face obstacles, and yet they persevere with unwavering determination.

But life is ever-changing, and so is Rey's. In "Moving to the US," we witness a pivotal shift in his journey as he embarks on a new chapter in an unfamiliar land. The subsequent chapter, "A Year of Wonders in the United States: Cockroach Strikes Back," brings laughter and tears as Rey confronts the challenges of assimilation, embracing the beauty of diversity.

This book captures the essence of Rey's memories, emotions, and personal growth. It serves as a bridge between cultures, enabling young readers to step into Rey's shoes and experience the world through his eyes. As they accompany him on this remarkable voyage, they will gain an appreciation for the courage it takes to embrace change and the strength derived from cultural roots.

"Rey's Transcontinental Tale" is an invitation to embrace diversity, cultivate empathy, and celebrate the unique stories that shape each one of us. It is a tribute to the resilience of the human spirit and a reminder that, despite the distances that separate us, our shared experiences bind us together as one global family. So, dear reader, join Rey as he embarks on this transformative odyssey—may his story resonate in your heart and inspire you to cherish the tapestry of life that connects us all.

Happy Birthday to me

On a sunny Tuesday morning, January 6th, 1976, I woke up to the melodious sound of my mom's singing, filling our small apartment. As I slowly opened my eyes, I saw her gracefully sweeping the floor with a contented smile. "Happy birthday!" she exclaimed joyfully, as soon as she noticed that I was awake. Instantly, all traces of sleep vanished, and my heart swelled with excitement. Today was the day I had eagerly awaited my whole life - I was six years old.

You see, in our neighborhood, one couldn't go to school until they reached the age of six, and this day marked my entry into the world of education. The school year was still a few months away, but the anticipation was too much to bear. I knew that soon, I would be joining my older siblings and cousins in the great adventure of learning. When the time finally came, Mom made sure to make me feel extra special. She had managed to get me a brand new school uniform, and I had never had new clothes before. Being the youngest with two older brothers and cousins ahead of us, all my clothes had been hand-me-downs until now. But this time, I had something entirely my own, and it made me feel like a prince. My uniform was a delightful golden-yellow shirt, crisp white t-shirt, well-fitted short brown dress pants, comfortable brown socks, a smart brown belt, and shiny brown shoes that gleamed like polished gems. I felt like I was ready to conquer the world.

Mom held my hand tightly as we walked towards the school together. She had a smile of pride and tenderness as she looked down at me. "You're growing up so fast," she said, "Soon, you'll be walking to school on your own, but today, I want to make sure you arrive perfectly." I was slightly worried about the dusty yard in front of our apartment building, but Mom was meticulous, making sure my shirt was tucked in just right and dusting powder on me until my chest looked like a cloud of white. With her loving care, I walked as carefully as possible, determined to keep my shoes spotless.

As we made our way through the familiar streets, passing the house with the big mango tree, which I had climbed countless times, we approached the bustling intersection. Panama's traffic wasn't always easy to navigate, but with Mom's guidance, we safely crossed the street. The school building loomed ahead, already visible from the main road, and my heart filled with excitement and a touch of nervousness.

We arrived early, allowing me to have breakfast at the school. Each day, they served porridge, and although it was often a little burnt, I didn't mind. It was my special school breakfast, and I savored every spoonful. Stepping into my first class on the second floor, I felt a mix of curiosity and anticipation. Unlike American schools, in Panamanian schools, the teacher and classmates remained the same until high school. It meant that my classmates would become like a second family to me over the years.

My teacher surprised us with two rolls of ribbon – one bright red and the other soothing blue. As she called each of us, we approached her, and she cut a piece of ribbon, tying it on our wrists. The red ribbon adorned the right hand, and the blue ribbon adorned the left. Throughout the day, we would be asked to raise either hand, making us feel like secret agents on some special mission. While learning both right and left.

In this close-knit environment, we all carried our book bags with the necessary materials for our lessons. If someone ever forgot something, our teacher, with her heart of gold, would gladly lend what was needed. Her caring nature made us feel like a family, learning and growing together. I made it my mission to befriend every single classmate, and by the end of the first week, I had succeeded, except for one girl who didn't speak back to me. It became my personal challenge to change that. I approached her one day and asked if I could walk her home. Although she shrugged her shoulders, I took it as a yes. From that moment on, we became walking buddies, and though she rarely spoke during school hours, she became a chatterbox on our way home, sharing stories and laughs.

This year and the next, our journey to and from school together became a cherished routine, deepening our friendship beyond the classroom walls. As we learned and played, we formed bonds that would last a lifetime. And so, with my shiny shoes and a heart full of dreams, I embraced the adventure of education in our little school in Panama.

Vocabulary Words:

Melodious: (adjective) Having a pleasant, tuneful, and musical sound.

Anticipation: (noun) A feeling of excitement or expectation about something that is going to happen.

Eagerly: (adverb) In a manner showing great enthusiasm or eagerness.

Tucked: (verb) To put something in a particular place or position, often to keep it safe or neat.

Meticulous: (adjective) Showing great attention to detail; very careful and precise.

Gleamed: (verb) To shine brightly with a sparkling or reflected light.

Befriend: (verb) To become friends with someone or to act as a friend toward them.

Nervousness: (noun) The state of feeling uneasy, anxious, or worried about something.

Adorned: (verb) To decorate or add beauty to something by adding ornaments or embellishments.

Nurturing: (adjective) Providing care, support, and encouragement for growth and development.

Cherished: (adjective) Highly valued and treasured with deep affection.

Curiosity: (noun) A strong desire to know or learn something new; inquisitiveness.

Secret agents: (noun) Covert operatives involved in espionage or intelligence gathering.

Caring: (adjective) Showing kindness, concern, and empathy for the well-being of others.

Chatterbox: (noun) A person who talks a lot and often, especially about trivial or unimportant matters.

Super Mom

My mom was an extraordinary person. She had faced unimaginable challenges from a young age and had to fight for things that most people couldn't fathom. She found herself on her very own at 12 years old without a defender and had to struggle for her own sanity and well-being. Although I didn't witness her acts of courage firsthand, I heard countless stories that illustrated her indomitable spirit. One such story involved a fire that broke out in my uncle's apartment while they were all asleep. While others hurried to save themselves, Mom displayed her bravery by evacuating the building with the refrigerator in tow. Her feistiness and physical prowess were apparent in every aspect of her life. Even when she was dating my Dad, the youngest among his siblings, she fearlessly intervened when his older brother was bullying him. At that moment, she took control of the situation, making her presence both heard and felt.

To me, this fighter was the embodiment of love and devotion, but she was also a no-nonsense parent. Her values were shaped by the suffering she had endured, and in times of hardship, her determination and self-encouragement always prevailed. I remember a particular day when Mom took me to a little convenience store. There, she purchased what was known as a "pavito" - a small bag of rice, a hot dog, and a bottle cap of oil - all for just $0.25. This humble purchase would sustain our family for a day. Upon returning home, she would cook the rice, cut the single hot dog into small pieces, and add tomato paste, onions, and seasoning to create a simple but flavorful meal.

The convenience store fascinated me, and the following day, I ventured there alone to gaze at the array of food that tempted my taste buds. However, I knew better than to touch anything. The consequences that awaited me for breaking the rules were far more severe than I was willing to endure. On my way back, a teenager deliberately pushed me, causing me to stumble and fall to the ground. Despite the unfairness of the situation, I quickly regained my footing, determined to stand my ground against someone twice my age. But my bravery was short-lived, as I was mercilessly beaten by the teenage boy. He laughed mockingly as I struggled to rise, asking if I wanted more. Discouraged and bruised, I trudged home and recounted the incident to Mom, whose anger grew with each word. She demanded to know the location of the boy and instructed my oldest brother to accompany me. My brother's face lit up with excitement, and although I was oblivious to the reason behind his smile, I welcomed his support.

As we approached the spot where my adversary lingered, Mom did something I never expected. In an effort to teach a vital life lesson, she directed me to confront the teenage boy once again. This time, however, she watched intently. Her message was clear: Never initiate a fight, always strive to be kind and courteous, and demonstrate the good manners you've been taught. But when someone strikes you, defend yourself. With a mixture of fear and determination, I entered the proverbial ring for round two. The boy delivered another relentless assault, and once again, I found myself sprawled on the ground. It was at that moment that Mom turned to my oldest brother and uttered the words, "Your turn." To my surprise, my brother, who seemed intimately acquainted with this way of life, stepped into the imaginary ring as a conquering hero. He fearlessly fought off the other boy, asserting his dominance. As he emerged victorious and walked away, he declared, "If you mess with my brother, you mess with all of us." Never had I felt prouder to be part of a family where, despite our occasional squabbles, we fiercely protected and fought for one another.

That incident marked a turning point in my life. It taught me the importance of self-defense and standing up for oneself. While my mom's approach may have seemed unconventional, it was an invaluable lesson that prepared me for the challenges I would face in the years to come. I learned that courage isn't just about physical strength but also about resilience and the ability to rise again after being knocked down. As I grew older, I carried my mom's teachings with me, always remembering her indomitable spirit and the lessons she imparted. I embraced opportunities to help others and be a voice for those who couldn't speak up for themselves.

Years later, as I stood at the threshold of adulthood, I couldn't help but reflect on the profound impact my mom had made in shaping the person I had become. She had been more than a parent to me; she was my unwavering rock, my guiding light, and the source of boundless inspiration. Through her own life's journey, she had imparted to me the invaluable lessons of bravery and sacrifice, teaching me the true meaning of resilience. With her legacy embedded deep within my heart, I faced life's challenges head-on, pushing myself to the limits, fueled by the unwavering belief that I possessed the strength to conquer any obstacle. It was as if my mom's indomitable spirit accompanied me every step of the way, a constant reminder to never back down, to hold onto my convictions, and to fiercely fight for what I believed in

In the end, my mom's story goes beyond her acts of bravery and her remarkable resilience. It is a story of love, strength, and unwavering devotion. It is a story that continues to inspire me and countless others to embrace life's challenges with courage and to always fight for a better tomorrow. And as I continue on my own journey, I know that my mom's teaching will forever be by my side, guiding me and reminding me that I, too, can be extraordinary.

Vocabulary words:

Indomitable: Impossible to defeat or subdue; unconquerable.

Feisty: Lively, determined, and full of spirit.

Prowess: Exceptional or superior ability, skill, or strength.

Fearless: Without fear or hesitation; brave.

Bullying: The act of using strength or power to intimidate or mistreat others.

Devotion: Deep love, loyalty, or dedication.

No-nonsense: Practical and efficient; focused on results rather than frivolity.

Endured: Suffered patiently or persistently through challenging circumstances.

Prevailed: Triumphed or emerged as the ultimate winner.

Humble: Modest or unpretentious in nature or appearance.

Array: A varied or diverse collection or display of things.

Consequences: The outcomes or results of one's actions.

Deliberately: Intentionally or purposefully.

Adversary: An opponent or enemy.

Intently: With great concentration, focus, or attention.

Proverbial: Widely known or referred to, often as a proverb or saying.

Relentless: Unyielding or persistent in intensity or severity.

Sprawled: Spread out in a relaxed or ungainly manner.

Fiercely: With intense or passionate determination.

Squabbles: Minor arguments or disagreements.

It Starts Here

A t eight years old, I lived in Panama on an Army base called Cocoli. One day, my two big brothers decided to have a walk in the jungle. My brothers were always picking on me, calling me names, and hitting me. But if I kept a reasonable distance from them, I could run away if they decided to chase me away. Panama was an enchanting place. While we walked in the jungle, many howler monkeys were jumping from tree to tree. They seemed not to like our presence because they would scream louder the further we walked into the jungle. The vibrant green canopy above us seemed alive, with their wild calls echoing through the dense foliage.

Whenever we walked close to a stream of water, some orange crabs marched on with a great multitude following. Watching these tiny creatures scuttle along the banks was a fascinating sight, forming a colorful parade. In the streams, I could see all kinds of fish darting through the crystal-clear water, and even freshwater shrimp would lazily swim by. When I looked up, a vast array of birds graced the treetops, with macaws, toucans, and parrots adding bursts of vibrant colors to the emerald landscape.

As we delved deeper into the jungle, my brothers stayed on the trail, seemingly unafraid. This was my first time walking in the jungle, and as long as my brothers were unafraid, I found no reason to fear. Every once in a while, my brothers would turn around and tell me to go back home, then start running in my direction. With a racing heart, I would quickly turn around and begin to run as fast as I could. When they would relent from chasing me, I would catch my breath and cautiously resume following them.

At one point, my brothers turned around and started running in my direction at full speed. Panic surged through me as I tried to match their pace, but at eight years old, there was no way I could outrun them. Fear gripped me, and I thought maybe they had me follow them on purpose. It was probably their idea to hurt me in the jungle, and no one would ever know. I ran even faster, my little legs pumping as hard as they could, desperate to escape their reach.

When I thought I was a goner, they passed me and kept running. Confusion mingled with relief as I watched their retreating figures. It didn't make sense. Why did they run toward me only to leave me behind? Curiosity stirred within me, and I decided to turn back around and continue following the path in the opposite direction from where my brothers were running.

Walking cautiously, I ventured deeper into the jungle, my senses heightened. The air was thick with the earthy scent of the rainforest, and the sounds of chirping insects and rustling leaves surrounded me. As I walked for about five minutes, I suddenly froze in my tracks. In front of me, a massive snake slithered along the ground, its sinewy body weaving through the undergrowth. My heart pounded in my chest, and without a second thought, I turned and sprinted away, my survival instincts kicking in.

I kept following the path, my mind racing with worry. But as I pressed forward, I realized that something was amiss. The jungle slowly gave way to unfamiliar terrain. Instead of the dense vegetation, I found myself walking on old paved roads partially reclaimed by nature. I had unknowingly strayed into the off-limits portion of the Army base.

3

Cocoli, the old base, was built by the personnel on the construction of a Third Locks Project at Miraflores Locks in late 1939. All the houses and buildings were made of wood, and as the new base, Fort Clayton, was established, the major facilities were relocated there. The homes in Cocoli were slowly being reclaimed by the encroaching jungle, creating an eerie yet intriguing atmosphere.

Though disoriented, I felt a glimmer of hope. The old roads were familiar, and I was sure I could find my house from where I was. But then, a particular house caught my attention. It had a magnificent mango tree growing in front of it. The tree was heavy with ripe mangoes, their tantalizing scent filling the air. Being mango season and with no one around, the fruits were almost touching the ground, tempting me with their juicy sweetness.

Unable to resist the allure, I approached the tree and climbed onto its sturdy branches. With wide eyes and a grumbling stomach, I began plucking and devouring the ripe, golden orange mangoes. The sweetness exploded on my taste buds, filling me with sheer delight. Lost in the moment, I ate to my heart's content, the mangoes satisfying my hunger and bringing me a sense of pure joy.

Satiated, I settled into a comfortable spot under the shady canopy of the mango tree. The day had taken unexpected turns, and fatigue overwhelmed me. Lulled by the quiet rustling of leaves and the distant hum of nature, I soon drifted off to sleep. However, my peaceful slumber was abruptly interrupted—a sharp pain shot through my arm, jolting me awake. Startled, I realized I had fallen asleep in an environment teeming with life, including bull ants. I hurriedly crawled out from under the tree, brushing away any lingering insects, and began sprinting toward home, my heart racing with a mixture of fear and urgency.

With each step, I traversed the old paved roads with no city lights to cast shadows around me. Thoughts of wild pumas, snakes, and jaguars haunted my mind, adding to the urgency of my escape. I knew that if I managed to survive the treacherous wilderness, I would have to face the consequences of worrying my parents. My feet pounded against the pavement, and beads of sweat trickled down my forehead. I pleaded with God, praying for forgiveness and to have a great story to avoid a whopping. Finally, as I approached our house, a sense of relief and dread washed over me simultaneously.

Taking a deep breath, I summoned the courage to knock on the door. The sound echoed through the quiet night, and after a few moments, my Dad opened it. His stern gaze met mine, and my heart sank. I would have preferred if it was Mom, as her soothing presence would have offered a glimmer of hope at that moment. But it had to be Dad, and I knew his disappointment would be a heavy burden. He didn't let me in right away. Instead, he asked in a firm voice, "Do you know what time it is?" I realized the story I was about to tell had to be convincing and sincere. I wiped away my tears and began, "Dad, I was following my brothers, and suddenly, they started running towards me and kept going. I've been trying to get home ever since, and I was afraid that a wild animal would get me before I reached home."

My voice quivered, and genuine fear laced my words. Tears welled up again, flowing freely down my cheeks. In that vulnerable moment, I heard my mother's soft, reassuring voice say, "Come in, Rey. Would you like something to eat?" Her compassion provided solace in the midst of my turmoil. I mustered a weak smile and replied, "No, Mom. I am still too afraid, and my stomach hasn't settled yet."

My dad motioned my two big brothers to go to his room, their expressions a mix of guilt and anticipation. I knew what awaited them there, and I couldn't help but feel a strange sense of satisfaction in knowing their actions would be addressed. As I entered the warmth and safety of our home, my tears continued to flow, a mixture of relief and remorse.

And so, my adventures continued, filled with both thrilling discoveries and valuable life lessons. The jungles of Panama became a canvas for growth and resilience.

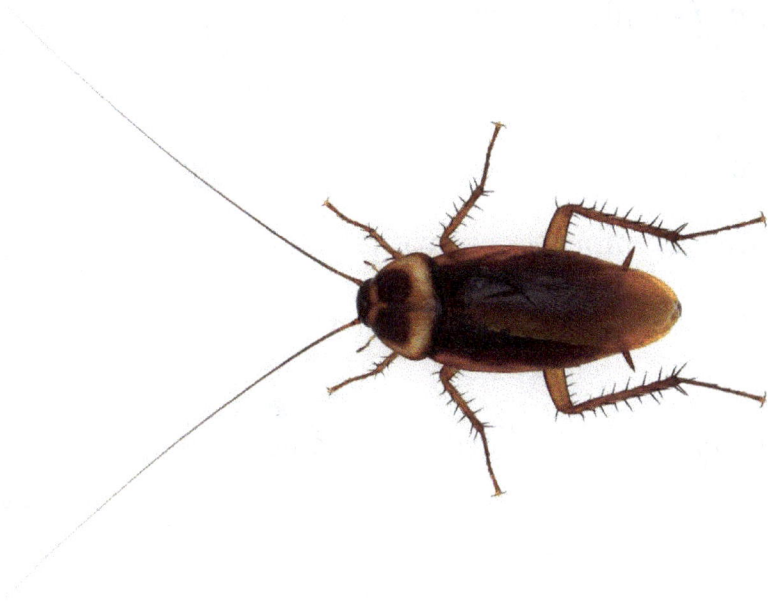

Vocabulary words:

Genuine: Authentic or real.

Encroaching: Gradually advancing or intruding upon something.

Teeming: Abundantly filled or swarming with something.

Treacherous: Dangerous or unpredictable.

Satiated - Fully satisfied or gratified.

Lulled - Calmed or soothed into a state of relaxation.

Traversed - Passed across, over, or through.

Solace - Comfort or consolation in a time of distress.

Mustered - Gathered or summoned up (courage, strength, etc.).

Immaturity - Lack of maturity or emotional development.

Zultana and the Elementary School

Going to school at Fort Clayton was a lot of fun. On the first day, my mother walked the journey with me. I am trying to remember whether my brothers accompanied us, but I always cherished those moments spent with Mom. The walk was long, and we didn't have school buses to take us to school. Once we got on the main road, it was about an hour's journey before we reached the next road that took us to Fort Clayton.

A public swimming pool was the last remnant of the road before exiting Cocoli. It stood there, a symbol of joy and carefree moments amidst our struggles. As a Panamanian family, we were very poor. My dad joined the US Army to give us a chance to escape poverty. He had chronic asthma and often experienced wheezing, but he kept his condition hidden, soldiering on for our sake. Dad later confided in us, sharing that his greatest desire was to ensure we never went to bed hungry again. He believed that even if he died while serving, the insurance provided by the military would offer us a better life than what we currently had.

During one of his deployments, Mom took care of us on her own. It was a challenging time for her, juggling the responsibilities of parenting and household management. She worked tirelessly, making sure we had food on the table even if she had to ask others to help and, many times, making the clothes we wore. I remember her worn-out expression, but she never let her weariness show. She remained strong, a beacon of love and resilience in our lives.

When Dad returned, we moved to a high-rise building in Parque Lefevre, Panama. It was a significant change for us, transitioning from the simplicity of Rio Abajo to the bustling urban neighborhood. The high-rise offered a glimpse of a different world, with its concrete structures reaching for the sky. We were in awe of our new surroundings, but it also came with its own set of challenges.

Living in the high-rise building brought us new experiences and struggles. It was the first time my parents shopped at the commissary, a store that catered to military personnel and their families. They bought everything any of us could want to eat. Once we got home, the kitchen was filled with an abundance of groceries. Mom, determined to give us a taste of what we had been missing, cooked a meal fit for royalty—the rich aromas wafted through our small apartment, filling every nook and cranny. Our anticipation grew with each passing minute.

However, when the food was finally served, we couldn't eat. The sight of such plenty overwhelmed us. We had never seen that much food before, and instead of opening our appetites, it made us feel sick to our stomachs. The stark reality of scarcity had shaped our relationship with food and was a difficult barrier to overcome. We learned, with time, to appreciate and savor the abundance that was now available to us, but it was a gradual process of adjusting our mindset.

While we eventually learned to love our new home, it had difficulties. For some reason, the high-rise building lacked an elevator, and we resided on the fifth floor. For a time, Mom had to be carried up the five flights of stairs whenever she went out or returned home. The only people who could help Mom was Dad and my two older brothers since the rest of us were too little. Each step they climbed was a testament to our love and dedication to our family.

During our time in that high-rise building, we experienced one of the most heart-wrenching losses—the passing of our best friend. Our beloved family dog, Zultana, had been with us through thick and thin. She was a source of comfort, a companion who never judged us—losing her left a void in our hearts that was difficult to fill. We mourned the loss as a family, holding onto the memories and the unconditional love Zultana had given us.

Zultana was a mixed dog, a unique blend of breeds that made her stand out. Her vibrant red fur and white patch around her neck made her a beautiful sight to behold. But it was her remarkable personality that truly set her apart. She seemed to possess a sense of understanding and loyalty that went beyond what was expected of a typical dog. In fact, the stories Mom shared about her suggested that Zultana had been more than just a pet to us.

Mom would often reminisce about Zultana's role as our nanny when we were still in diapers. Whenever we wandered into an area Mom deemed unsafe, Zultana would gently grab our diapers and guide us back to safety. In those moments, she became our guardian and protector, watching over us with a keen sense of responsibility. Due to our poverty, there were times when the caregiver role fell upon Zultana for short periods. She filled those moments with unwavering love and care, proving she was more than just a dog to us.

However, there came a time when our family faced a difficult decision. With limited resources and insufficient food to feed everyone, Mom and Dad decided they would have to give Zultana away. They believed it was the best choice for her and our family. They searched for someone who could provide Zultana with a better life, but everyone in our impoverished community was struggling just like us. Eventually, they involved our grandfather in the decision-making process, hoping he could find a solution.

One day, Granddad came by and took Zultana away. We all cried, unable to bear the thought of being separated from our beloved canine companion. Our parents' intentions were born out of love, but our hearts ached for the loss of Zultana's presence. We were unsure of what Granddad would do with her, but as time passed, we received a surprising revelation. Granddad had taken her to a place called Cerro Azul, a wealthy neighborhood where he hoped she would find a new home with an affluent American family.

To our astonishment, Zultana walked back home to us. She had traveled an incredible 25 miles, determined to reunite with her family. Her unwavering loyalty and deep attachment to us were evident in every step she took. Witnessing her remarkable journey, Mom and Dad knew that Zultana was meant to stay with us, no matter what challenges we faced. From that day forward, Zultana remained an integral part of our family, her unwavering presence a symbol of love and devotion. As the years went by, Zultana continued to prove her incredible worth. On the last day of her life, she accomplished more than she ever had before. It was a day filled with both tragedy and heroism.

My oldest brother was taking out the trash and had to cross a busy street to reach the dumpster. When he turned to cross back, he was taken by surprise as a car approached at high speed, leaving him little time to react. Sensing the impending danger, Zultana sprang into action. With lightning speed and unwavering bravery, she launched herself into the air, using her body as a shield to propel my brother out of harm's way.

Tragically, Zultana bore the full impact of the collision. The car ran over her, causing severe injuries to her stomach. My two older brothers, filled with panic and desperation, swiftly carried her up the five flights of stairs to our apartment. They gently laid her on the floor, surrounded by the family she had loved and protected for so long. In those final moments, we all gathered around her, tears streaming down our faces as we whispered words of gratitude and love. Zultana listened to our heartfelt expressions, her eyes reflecting the depth of her understanding and devotion. With a peaceful sigh, she quietly left us, her spirit forever etched in our hearts.

This long walk to school would have been difficult for Zultana, our loyal mixed-breed dog. She would have followed and waited patiently for me to finish school so we could walk back home together. The journey to school was tiring, especially on hot days. At Fort Clayton, the school schedule differed from that of Panamanian schools. On Wednesdays, the elementary school finished earlier than the junior high school, giving me some extra time at home on those afternoons. On one fateful Wednesday, I arrived home before my other siblings, who were still in junior high school. Our dad owned a cherished 1957 Chevy, a car he had longed for but could only afford once we moved to Cocoli. It had become his pride and joy, a symbol of his hard work and determination.

I watched my oldest brother often sit in the driver's seat and pretend to drive, imagining the freedom and thrill of being behind the wheel. With no one else at home and feeling a sense of curiosity, I decided to join in on the make-believe adventure. Climbing into the front seat, I positioned myself and started mimicking my brother's actions, feeling a surge of excitement as I pretended to drive like him.

However, being only eight years old, I didn't realize that when my brother pretended to drive, he didn't touch the gears or start the engine. Oblivious to this crucial detail, I inadvertently shifted the gear, and to my surprise, the car began to move. Panic gripped me as I realized I had no idea how to stop the car, and its speed started to increase. Living at the top of a hill only exacerbated the situation. Fear coursed through my veins as I desperately searched for a solution. In a split second, I made a decision that felt instinctual – I had to get out of the moving car. With my heart pounding, I mustered all my courage and jumped out, tumbling onto the pavement. As I watched in horror, the car continued its path, picking up speed and eventually becoming airborne. It crashed through the chapel's stained glass window at the bottom of the hill, causing a cacophony of shattering glass and chaos.

At that moment, I stood frozen, my heart sinking as I comprehended the magnitude of the damage I had caused. The realization of the trouble I would be in washed over me, and panic gripped my young mind. As the dust settled, I knew I had to face the consequences of my impulsive actions. Summoning all the courage I could muster, I reached for the phone and dialed my dad's number at his workplace. The tremor in my voice betrayed my fear as I informed him I had a sleepover at a friend's house and wouldn't return home until the next day. Unaware of the events that had unfolded, my dad thanked me for the reminder and assured me it was all right. Desperate to buy some time and escape the wrath I anticipated, I quickly called a friend, pleading for an impromptu sleepover, and began to pack my belongings, creating the illusion of an overnight stay. The following day, I soon discovered that my oldest brother had been severely beaten for the destruction of Dad's prized possession.

Vocabulary words:

Loyal - Faithful and devoted; showing constant support or allegiance.

Companionship - The state of being with someone as a friend or partner.

Tiring - Causing fatigue or weariness.

Cherished - Highly valued and deeply appreciated.

Determination - Firmness of purpose; a strong resolve.

Thrill - A feeling of excitement or exhilaration.

Inadvertently - Accidentally or unintentionally.

Exacerbate - To make a problem, situation, or condition worse.

Tremor - A slight shaking or quivering movement.

Repercussions - Consequences or effects that arise as a result of an action or event.

Faithful - Loyal and steadfast; reliable.

Schedule - A plan or timetable for a series of events or activities.

Pretend - To make-believe or imitate something for fun or as a game.

Curiosity - A strong desire to know or learn something.

Instinct - An innate, natural impulse or behavior.

Panic - Sudden overwhelming fear or anxiety.

Escalate - To increase rapidly or intensify.

Repercussions - Unintended consequences or effects, typically negative ones.

Chaos - Complete disorder or confusion.

Punishment - A penalty or consequence given as a result of wrongdoing or disobedience.

Getting Used to My Surroundings

Within one school year, I found myself forming a diverse group of friends, and my inquisitive nature led me to explore everything around me. Living on an Army base opened up numerous opportunities, from joining a soccer team (which I quickly discovered I had little talent for) to simply hanging out with friends and embracing the sense of community.

As friendships grew, so did the range of experiences we shared. One day, a friend of mine attempted to introduce me to smoking. Curiosity got the better of me, and I watched with fascination as he took a long drag on a cigarette, exhaling a cloud of smoke. With a sense of adventure, he passed the cigarette to me, encouraging me to try it. I mimicked his actions without thinking twice, bringing the cigarette to my lips and inhaling deeply. However, the sensation overwhelmed my inexperienced lungs, and I found myself coughing uncontrollably. In a rush of realization, I quickly threw the cigarette to the ground and stomped on it, crushing it until it merged with the earth beneath my feet. Turning to my friend, I declared firmly, "This is stupid, and I'll never do that again."

As time passed, I unintentionally became the leader of our little pack. It was a peculiar circumstance, given that I barely knew how to speak English while all the other kids were native English speakers. Yet, through shared experiences and a natural sense of curiosity, I found myself taking charge. We embarked on adventures together, exploring every nook and cranny of the Army base. Our youthful energy led us to the off-limits zone, where we stumbled upon an old, abandoned school building. Excitement filled the air as we decided to test our courage by breaking the windows, unleashing a chorus of shattering glass.

However, our raucous adventure was noticed. The breaking glass echoes attracted the attention of a passing Military Police officer, who followed the sound to our location. As his patrol car screeched to a halt outside, panic engulfed me. Peering through a broken window, I caught a glimpse of the officer making his way up the stairs, each step bringing him closer. Faced with the imminent threat of capture, I quickly decided to remain silent and conceal my presence.

While I successfully avoided capture, fate was not as kind to the others and my younger brother, who had been trailing behind us throughout our misadventure. I had urged him to go home when he initially followed. However, his unwavering determination led him to stay by my side, seeking a taste of the excitement we all seemed to embrace. As the Military Police officer began his investigation, I held my breath, praying for my hidden presence to go unnoticed. I knew the officer would start returning the kids from where we were until the farthest house that was mine. I ran home as fast as my little feet could fly.

Upon reaching our house, I found Dad sitting in the living room, engrossed in the newspaper. Desperately trying to appear nonchalant, I walked into the kitchen, hastily beginning to wash the dishes. I engaged Dad in casual conversation, hoping to distract him from the impending trouble that loomed over us. Before he could respond, a firm knock on the door shattered the fragile peace of the moment. My heart skipped a beat as I recognized the silhouette of the Military Police officer through the frosted glass. My younger brother stood beside him, a mix of apprehension and guilt etched on his face. Dad opened the door, his expression turning from confusion to disappointment as the officer explained the situation and mentioned his intent to report the incident to Dad's superiors. With a heavy sigh, Dad closed the door, his gaze stern and unforgiving.

In a swift motion, Dad grabbed my younger brother by the ear, his voice stern and filled with authority. A swift beating followed a form of discipline meant to teach a valuable lesson. As they reentered the living room, my younger brother, desperate to shift the blame away from himself, pointed a trembling finger at me, uttering, "Dad, it was all Rey's idea." Dad's eyes flickered with a mix of sternness and understanding. His voice carried the weight of experience and wisdom as he responded with a West Indian accent, *"Boy, yuh brodder 'ave been right yah, diligently washin' di dishes. Since yuh waan fi lie an' shift di blame onto him, yuh gwine receive anodder whoopin', fi lyin' an' fi tryin' fi shift responsibility."* ("Boy, your brother has been right here, diligently washing the dishes. Since you want to lie and shift the blame onto him, you are going to receive another whooping for lying and for trying to shift responsibility.")

Vocabulary words:

Diverse - Showing a great deal of variety or difference.

Embrace - To accept willingly and wholeheartedly.

Unintentionally - Happening without deliberate intent or planning.

Raucous - Making a disturbingly harsh and loud noise; rowdy or disorderly.

Chorus - A simultaneous utterance or repetition of words or sounds by a group of people.

Conceal - To hide or keep a secret.

Precious - Of great value; cherished.

Engrossed - Fully absorbed or deeply involved in something.

Apprehension - Anxiety or fear that something wrong or unpleasant will happen.

Authority - The power to give orders or make decisions; the ability to enforce obedience.

Living in Rio Abajo

Rio Abajo, a city renowned for its pervasive poverty, we, as children, were oblivious to the weight of our economic struggles. In our youthful innocence, we perceived ourselves as being as rich as anyone else, for our wealth lay not in material possessions but in the bonds we shared and the joy we found in simple pleasures. Our surroundings may have painted a picture of poverty, but we were oblivious to the limitations it imposed upon us. We reveled in the love and support of our families and friends, cherishing the bonds that held us together.

Our first apartment complex, perched on the second floor of the first building, embodied the struggles we faced. Its exterior was devoid of a specific paint color, as layers of paint could be seen peeling off, exposing the wear and tear of time. The stairway, located towards the back of the building, led us to a porch that served as a connector to all the apartments on the second floor. Inside our humble abode, we made the most of our limited space. We had two rooms and a small cooking area. The first room served as a multifunctional space—a living room during the day and a dining area at mealtimes. In the evenings, the room transformed into a cozy haven where our family gathered to share stories and watch TV together.

The second room was where the magic happened. It was a shared bedroom that accommodated Mom, Dad, my four brothers, and one sister. The room was filled with makeshift beds, handcrafted from salvaged pieces of wood and concrete bricks. Each bed represented the resourcefulness and determination of our family to make the most out of what little we had. The room, although crowded, overflowed with love and affection. There were four beds in the room. One bunk bed where the four boys slept, A small bed in the corner for the only sister, and a bed for Mom and Dad.

In the small cooking area, we were fortunate to have a refrigerator with a freezer. While it may have been old and showing signs of wear, it was a prized possession. Many families in our neighborhood didn't have the luxury of a refrigerator, forcing them to find alternative ways to preserve food. We recognized the blessing we had, especially during the scorching summer months when cold drinks and frozen treats offered temporary relief from the sweltering heat. With ingenuity, we transformed simple Kool-Aid into frozen cups, delighting the neighborhood children who eagerly bought them for just a few pennies.

Towards the back of the apartment, we shared communal bathrooms and showers with the other families in the building. These shared facilities taught us the values of patience, understanding, and cooperation. We learned to take turns, waiting for our chance to use the bathroom or shower, always mindful that someone else might be waiting as well. It was in these shared spaces that we built connections with our neighbors, exchanging stories and laughter, finding solace in the midst of our shared struggles.

The apartment's windows, adorned with old-fashioned pane glass, were both a portal to the outside world and a reminder of the limitations we faced. Through the gaps in the exterior panels, slivers of light seeped into our humble abode, casting intricate patterns on the worn wooden floors. However, it was during the thunderstorms that these windows became truly magical. The lightning danced across the sky, illuminating the darkened room through the tiny holes in the walls. The thunder rumbled, and the rain tapped on the exposed tin roof, creating a symphony that no musician could match.

In our impoverished state, we found beauty in the discarded and forgotten. Recycling wasn't a concept that was widely practiced during those times, but we instinctively understood the value of repurposing. We breathed new life into old materials, turning them into cherished treasures. On one special occasion, all the kids in our neighborhood came together in front of our apartment building to embark on an exciting project. My older brothers wanted to create a unique and captivating structure using cardboard boxes that they collected. As they brainstormed different ideas, they decided to connect the boxes in a specific way, forming a remarkable shape called a logarithmic spiral. *(We didn't know this word back then)*.

To construct this extraordinary structure, they connected the boxes at a slight angle, making sure each box was slightly smaller than the one before it. This clever arrangement allowed the boxes to form a captivating spiral shape, similar to the patterns found in seashells and other natural wonders. As we crawled into this fascinating structure, we couldn't help but marvel at the captivating beauty of the logarithmic spiral. The boxes were arranged in such a way that they created a gradual curve, spiraling inward as we moved towards the center. It felt as if we were exploring a secret passage leading to a hidden treasure. Inside the structure, the spiraling arrangement made the space feel cozy and intimate. The boxes formed a winding path, guiding us through the structure and creating an atmosphere of adventure and discovery. It was a place where our imaginations could soar, and new stories could unfold. Once we got to the center of the structure, there was a hidden compartment that you could only find by pushing the right boxes to enter. Each of us contributed to the creation of this unique structure, and together we reveled in the joy of exploration and play.

Mother's Day and Father's Day held special significance in our household. Weeks before these celebrations, my brothers and sister scoured through old magazines, tearing out colorful pages filled with images of far-off places and smiling faces. With scissors, glue, and boundless creativity, we transformed those pages into heartfelt cards, expressing our love and gratitude for our parents.

When my two older brothers stumbled upon an old, unusable bicycle, they saw it not just as an abandoned relic but as an opportunity for innovation. With unwavering determination, they carefully dismantled the bike, salvaging the usable parts. Piece by piece, they painstakingly put together a new creation—a unique bicycle. Even a single skate, designed to fit all sizes, held the promise of transformation in their imaginative hands. As my brothers separated the two parts and fastened them to a sturdy board, a makeshift scooter emerged. They skillfully repurposed the skate into a vehicle that became a cherished possession, transporting them to countless adventures and creating lasting memories.

Our poverty was a daily reminder of the challenges we faced, but within the walls of our humble abode, we discovered the boundless power of resilience, and creativity. It was in these moments of ingenuity, shared experiences, and unwavering familial support that we found solace and the strength to rise above our circumstances. And as we grew older, we carried these lessons in our hearts, forever grateful for the hardships that shaped us into the resilient individuals we became.

Vocabulary words:

Devoid: Completely lacking or empty of something. For example, a room devoid of furniture has no furniture at all.

Unity: The state of being together or joined as a whole. It means working together and supporting one another.

Resilience: The ability to bounce back or recover quickly from difficulties or challenges. It means being strong and not giving up easily.

Ingenuity: Being clever, creative, and resourceful in solving problems or coming up with new ideas. It means thinking outside the box.

Solace: Comfort or relief from sadness, loneliness, or distress. It means finding comfort and peace during difficult times.

Scarcity: When something is not readily available or in short supply. It means there isn't enough of something.

Resourcefulness: The ability to find clever and creative ways to use materials or solve problems. It means making the most of what you have.

Multifunctional: Something that can be used for many different purposes or has multiple functions. It means being versatile and having more than one use.

Repurposed: When an object or material is used for a different purpose than what it was originally intended for. It means giving something a new use instead of throwing it away.

Sweltering: Extremely hot or uncomfortably hot weather. It means feeling very hot and sweaty.

Logarithmic spiral: A special type of spiral with a curved pattern that gets wider as it moves away from the center. It is found in nature, like the shape of a seashell or a nautilus shell.

Encountering Panama's Wildlife

Nestled in the vibrant landscapes of Cocoli, my childhood was imbued with a profound connection to the natural world. This enchanting place teemed with an abundance of wildlife, ensuring that each day brought forth encounters with an array of fascinating creatures. Among the many captivating beings that graced our surroundings, the capybara stood as a constant presence, capturing our hearts with its unique charm. Belonging to the rodent family, capybaras effortlessly commanded attention with their commanding size. Their stocky bodies, short legs, and round heads bestowed upon them a distinct appearance, one that exuded an undeniable allure. But it was their coarse fur, adorned in hues that ranged from reddish-brown to dark brown, that truly accentuated their remarkable beauty. These gentle giants seemed to effortlessly blend into their surroundings, their earthy tones harmonizing with the lush foliage and rippling waters that defined their habitat.

Despite their classification as rodents, capybaras possessed a captivating demeanor that set them apart from their smaller relatives. Their docile nature and serene countenance bestowed upon them an air of tranquility, radiating a sense of calm to all those fortunate enough to witness their presence. In the languid afternoons of our childhood, we would often observe capybaras leisurely traversing the banks of nearby rivers or peacefully basking under the warm sun. Their unhurried movements reflected a pearl of innate wisdom, as if they understood the beauty of embracing life's gentle rhythm.

While capybaras, with their endearing presence, were a familiar sight in our neighborhood, there were rare moments that gifted us with extraordinary encounters. One such mesmerizing experience unfolded when we unexpectedly stumbled upon an anteater leisurely strolling down the street. It's elongated snout and bushy tail added to its intriguing allure, while its sharp claws served as a reminder of its formidable defenses. We were well aware of the need to maintain a respectful distance, recognizing that provoking or disturbing this majestic creature could lead to unintended consequences. With a mix of awe and admiration, we quietly observed its relaxed walk, marveling at the unique features and enigmatic nature of this enchanting creature.

At one point, my parents decided to hire a cleaning lady to assist with household chores. She was a descendant of the Guna tribe, who referred to themselves as Tule. It was through her that we gained insights into her rich cultural heritage and learned more about the unique traditions of the Guna people. On a particular day, my brother spotted an incredibly large iguana, and our help encouraged him to catch it. Little did we know that the iguana possessed a formidable weapon in its tail. With one swift motion, the iguana lashed its tail like a whip, leaving a lasting scar on my brother's skin. The encounter taught us to respect the power and defense mechanisms of these reptilian creatures. Yet, with all its ferocity, my brothers caught the animal, and our cleaning lady, skilled in her culinary prowess, proceeded to cook the iguana, transforming it into a delicacy. She even hung the iguana eggs on the clothesline to dry, which she deemed as a special treat. While some were adventurous enough to try the reptilian-flavored meat, I hesitated when it came to sampling the eggs.

In another thrilling instance, my oldest brother's remarkable agility prompted him to embark on a daring feat—climbing a towering coconut tree in pursuit of its luscious fruits. With determination in his eyes, he skillfully ascended the swaying trunk, inch by inch. However, just as he reached the pinnacle, a sudden flurry of wings and piercing screeches filled the air as a group of fruit bats emerged from the branches. Startled by their unexpected appearance, my brother's grip faltered, and with a gasp of surprise, he plummeted toward the ground. Miraculously, his fall was cushioned by the soft earth, sparing him from serious harm. Though shaken, he emerged with only minor injuries.

Among the captivating residents of Panama's diverse wildlife, the sloths held a special place in our hearts. Revered for their unhurried movements and impressive climbing abilities, these gentle creatures enchanted us with their serene demeanor. Contrary to their leisurely reputation, we discovered that sloths possessed a hidden talent for surprising agility when faced with unexpected disturbances. Startled or feeling threatened, their usually slow-paced existence gave way to a burst of unexpected speed as they swiftly maneuvered through the branches. Witnessing this sudden burst of energy was a remarkable sight, challenging our preconceived notions and reminding us of the hidden depths within every creature. As we observed the sloths' graceful ascent up the trees, their deliberate motions mirrored the unhurried rhythm of nature itself. Their tranquil presence served as a gentle reminder to embrace the slower pace of life, and to take the time to appreciate the beauty and simplicity that surrounds us.

Panama's rich biodiversity provided countless opportunities for unforgettable encounters with the animal kingdom. From the ever-present capybaras to the anteater, iguana, fruit bats, and fascinating sloths, each animal left an indelible mark on our lives, instilling in us a profound admiration for the natural world. These encounters taught us to respect and appreciate the unique characteristics and behaviors of the animals that share our planet.

Vocabulary words:

Agility: The ability to move quickly and easily with coordination and grace.

Biodiversity: The variety of plant and animal species that exist in a particular habitat or ecosystem.

Burst: A sudden and intense outpouring or increase in activity or energy.

Capybara: A large rodent with a stocky body, short legs, a round head, and coarse fur, native to Central and South America.

Culinary: Relating to cooking or the art of preparing food.

Culmination: The highest point, climax, or final stage of something; the end result or conclusion.

Delicacy: A choice or rare food item that is considered highly desirable or special.

Enigmatic: Mysterious, puzzling, or difficult to understand.

Ferocity: The state or quality of being fierce, savage, or aggressive; intense or extreme fierceness.

Formidable: Inspiring fear or respect through being impressively powerful, intense, or capable.

Intriguing: Arousing curiosity or interest; fascinating or captivating.

Prowess: Exceptional or superior skill or ability.

Reptilian: Relating to or characteristic of reptiles, a class of cold-blooded vertebrates that includes snakes, lizards, turtles, and crocodiles.

Serene: Calm, peaceful, and untroubled.

Tranquil: Calm, peaceful, and free from disturbance or agitation; serene and undisturbed.

I Like Sugar

Growing up in Cocoli, our home was a hub of family gatherings, particularly on my father's side. Despite the absence of my mother's side of the family within our home, my dad's two siblings and their extended family always seemed to find their way to our doorstep. The cultural disparities between my parents' backgrounds added an additional layer of complexity to our family dynamics. My dad, who identified as West Indian, often referred to my mother's side as "Spanish people," highlighting the stark differences in culture that existed between them. The Spanish and indigenous influence was prominent in my mother's family, from their spoken Spanish to their traditions, while my father's heritage celebrated the vibrant customs of the West Indies. These contrasting cultural backgrounds meant that interactions with my mother's side were infrequent, primarily limited to the occasions when we made an effort to visit them. This pattern of minimal connection persists to this day.

In contrast, my father's side of the family embodied a sense of unity and shared ownership. They believed that what belonged to Dad belonged to them all, and as a result, our home became a welcoming space for our cousins to gather and create cherished memories. One unforgettable afternoon, my cousin, who was significantly older than me, showcased his culinary prowess in our humble kitchen. He possessed an innate talent for cooking, and I, being the ever-curious youngster, yearned to learn his secret ingredients and techniques. As the mouthwatering aroma of a roasted chicken permeated the air, I observed my cousin's meticulous preparations. With great finesse, he opened the oven door, adorned with protective gloves, and expertly lifted the succulent bird from its resting place. In a move that piqued my interest, he delicately sprinkled a touch of brown sugar onto the chicken's glistening skin, imparting a hint of sweetness to the dish. Captivated by this seemingly magical transformation, I watched intently as he closed the oven door and momentarily left the kitchen.

Left alone in the midst of culinary intrigue, I couldn't resist the temptation that beckoned. I slipped on the gloves and gingerly pulled the chicken out of the oven, my youthful enthusiasm guiding my actions. With an innocent belief that more is always better, I liberally coated the entire bird with an abundance of brown sugar, convinced that this would elevate its flavors to unimaginable heights. Ignorant of the potential consequences that awaited, I gleefully returned the chicken to its rightful place in the oven, my heart brimming with anticipation of the gastronomic masterpiece that was surely about to unfold. Little did I realize that my culinary experimentation would soon take an unexpected turn.

Within the heated confines of the oven, the excessive amount of sugar ignited a fiery spectacle. As the flames danced and flickered, the kitchen quickly filled with thick plumes of smoke. Alarmed by the growing chaos, my cousin rushed back into the kitchen, his eyes widening in disbelief at the sight before him. In a panic, he attempted to extinguish the flames by opening the oven door, inadvertently fueling the fire's voracious appetite. The situation escalated rapidly, prompting a call to the local fire department. Soon, the shrill sirens echoed through the neighborhood as firefighters rushed to our home, equipped to combat the unexpected culinary inferno.

Fortunately, the swift response of the firefighters prevented the flames from spreading beyond the confines of the kitchen. The damage, although contained, was a stark reminder of the consequences that can arise from youthful curiosity and the mischievous allure of culinary experimentation. Amidst the lingering haze of smoke and the palpable tension, a secret remained hidden. No one ever found out that it was my innocent addition of sugar to the oven that had caused the unexpected fire. This clandestine detail, known only to me, added a layer of guilt and apprehension to the aftermath. It was a weight I carried silently, a lesson learned about the importance of taking responsibility for one's actions and the potential impact they can have on those around us.

Vocabulary Words:

Cherished: Highly valued and treasured.

Customs: Social or cultural practices and traditions that are typical of a particular group or community.

Culinary: Relating to cooking or the art of preparing food.

Disparities: Differences or contrasts, especially in relation to culture, background, or circumstances.

Endure: To withstand or survive through challenging circumstances or experiences.

Gastronomic: Relating to the art and science of good eating, particularly with regard to food and cooking.

Hub: A central point or gathering place.

Inferno: A large, intensely hot fire.

Meticulous: Showing great attention to detail; thorough and precise.

Mischievous: Playfully causing trouble or harm in a harmless or teasing way.

Palpable: Perceptible or noticeable; able to be felt or touched.

Prowess: Exceptional skill, talent, or ability.

Resilience: The ability to recover quickly from difficulties or setbacks; toughness.

Vibrant: Full of energy, enthusiasm, and liveliness.

Vivacious: Lively, spirited, and full of energy.

The Church and the Nail

Growing up in the 1970s, my family underwent a significant change in faith the year I was born, later in August. We transitioned from being Catholics, like many others in Latin America, to attending a church just down the street from our apartment. Despite our meager means, my brothers, sisters, and I always dressed in our best clothes for church, as did everyone else. We each owned only one pair of shoes, so when we wanted to play outside, we would take off our shoes. Even when it rained, we found joy in walking barefoot and playing in the refreshing downpour. In fact, whenever the rain started, all the neighborhood kids would gather outside, reveling in the fun it brought. Given the frequent rain showers in Panama, this became a way for us to make the most of what we had.

Attending church became a regular part of our routine. We went every night and even twice on Sundays. The church itself was perched on stilts, likely due to its proximity to a nearby river. Its weathered exterior matched the appearance of other buildings in the neighborhood, with peeling paint and a mismatched color palette. Inside, a single spacious room welcomed worshippers, its windows lacking panes. Handmade benches without backs lined the room, and at the front, an old piano that only the pastor played.

The people who gathered in that humble church were full of life, exuding a pure quality in their worship. The song services seemed to stretch on forever, accompanied by the pastor's skilled piano playing. However, my favorite part was always when the pastor took the pulpit to preach. This was when I found the most solace and often found myself drifting off to sleep, enveloped by the comforting sound of his voice.

One fateful night, a congregant unexpectedly stood up and urged everyone to go outside. Astonishingly, everyone complied with his request, and we all stood outside, watching in awe as the old building collapsed before our very eyes. As a child, I couldn't comprehend how that man knew what was about to happen, but I felt an immense relief that no one was hurt. Considering the age of the building and the fervent jumping and worship that took place within its walls, it was surprising that it hadn't collapsed sooner.

After my parents left for the United States, I found myself missing the experience of going to church. It had been something our family did together every day, and its absence left a void in my heart. Although my grandmother and aunt were still devout Catholics, they didn't attend any specific church. Determined to continue my spiritual journey, I approached my grandmother and requested permission to attend a church on a Sunday. However, she informed me that I would have to walk there and back, as it was too far for her to accompany me. Undeterred, I embarked on the journey, accompanied by my younger brother.

There was only one problem: I had no idea where our church had relocated. In a letter to my dad, my grandmother asked if he knew the new address, and within a week, we received a response. Armed with the newfound information, my brother and I made our way to the church, expecting to find another building. To my surprise, instead of a traditional structure, we discovered a large tent. The attendance had multiplied fivefold compared to when we had a building, and behind the pulpit area, they had erected two latrines. The lively music, which I had always enjoyed, still echoed through the air, but now the pastor no longer played the piano. Instead, the church had embraced guitars, drums, and a group of singers, infusing the atmosphere with an even greater sense of energy. What struck me the most was that the people remembered me and my younger brother, who had accompanied me on this journey. Although the pastor seemed to have taken a step back, allowing others to preach, I didn't doze off during the sermons anymore. At nine years old, I felt compelled to pay attention, recognizing that I was no longer a young child.

As we made our way home from the church one day, my brother and I stumbled upon an open field with medium-height grass. Thinking it would save us some time on our walk, we decided to cut through the field. However, about halfway across, disaster struck. I stepped on a board that had a protruding nail, which pierced through my shoe and lodged itself deep into my foot. The pain was excruciating, but I couldn't stay there, paralyzed by agony. With immense effort, I attempted to lift my foot off the nail, but the board came up with it. Realizing the gravity of the situation, I instructed my little brother to run back to our grandmother's house and seek help. Despite being just seven years old, he was my best friend and didn't hesitate for a moment. He sprinted off, leaving me alone in the field.

Minutes felt like an eternity as I endured the searing pain. I watched as my shoe filled with blood, feeling the heat of the day intensify. I desperately hoped for someone to pass by, someone who could offer assistance. Yet, to my dismay, no one appeared. Sweat poured down my face, mingling with tears of frustration and anguish. But just when I thought all hope was lost, a familiar figure came into view. It was my second eldest brother, running toward me at full speed. Streams of tears streaked his cheeks, a reflection of the sheer dread that had gripped him at the thought of losing me.

As he reached my side, he quickly assessed the situation. Without hesitation, he placed one foot on the board, causing a jolt of pain to surge through my body. Gripping me tightly, he instructed me to hold on as he summoned every ounce of strength within him. With a powerful lift, he raised me, his voice echoing with exertion. As he released me from the board's grip, he urged me to hop to a safer spot so we could assess the damage inflicted by the nail. We eventually reached a stone wall where I could sit down and carefully remove my shoe. As I had suspected, it was drenched in blood, but the wound inflicted by the nail had already begun to close. The resilience of the human body amazed me. My little brother finally caught up to us, and together, they helped me hobble back home. We decided not to tell Grandma or any of the adults what had transpired, and I'm grateful that I ultimately recovered without any severe consequences.

Vocabulary Words:

Meager - Lacking in quantity or quality; inadequate.

Reveling - Taking great pleasure or delight in something.

Proximity - Nearness in space, time, or relationship.

Weathered - Worn and damaged by exposure to the elements.

Mismatched - Not matching or harmonizing with something else.

Solace - Comfort or consolation in a time of distress or sadness.

Astonishingly - In a way that causes surprise or amazement.

Fervent - Displaying passionate intensity or enthusiasm.

Erupted - Broke out suddenly and violently.

Undeterred - Not discouraged or dissuaded.

Protruding - Sticking out or projecting from a surface.

Agony - Extreme physical or mental suffering.

Exertion - Physical or mental effort.

Gripping - Holding tightly or firmly.

Resilience - The ability to recover quickly from difficulties or adversity.

Consequences - The results or effects of an action or decision.

Dreams Unmet

I often found myself wondering about the Army's decision not to allow my dad to reenlist. When he initially joined the Army, he disclosed that he had two kids, aware that the number was seven. Also, having asthma and behavioral problems, children had affected his job opportunities. While still in the Army, the housing arrangements in Cocoli were intended for two families per building, but our family's size prompted the Army to merge the two units into one building into one. This larger space, though still modest, served as our haven. My siblings never uttered a complaint. In fact, our home became a hub of activity, accommodating not only our immediate family but also welcoming cousins who sought refuge with us. Our family of nine would occasionally expand to include 12 or 13 members. Little did I know those precious moments would become cherished memories, encapsulating the happiest times we would ever experience as a family.

After completing his service in the Army, Dad embarked on a journey to the United States in search of employment.

In Miami, Florida, he chanced upon a hiring sign adorning a high-rise building. Intrigued, he entered the premises and inquired about available positions. To his amazement, the manager offered him a job as a window washer on the spot. Dad had held various jobs in the past, ranging from a bus driver to a secretary, but now he found himself tasked with the responsibility of washing windows in the United States.

Filled with a sense of optimism, Dad arrived on his first day of work. Determination gleamed in his eyes as he ascended to the designated floor, ready to tackle the laborious task of window cleaning. Clad in his work clothes, he stepped onto the outer lift and embarked on his new venture. However, unbeknownst to him, a hidden fear lurked within his heart – a fear of heights. As the lift began its ascent, his nerves gradually intensified, causing his palms to perspire. Despite his best efforts to muster the courage, the sight of the towering heights overwhelmed him. After a mere 15 minutes, he realized that conquering this fear would require more than determination alone. Reluctantly, he made the difficult decision to step off the lift and approach the understanding manager. With a humble request for compensation, he bid farewell to the job that wasn't meant to be after just fifteen minutes.

The details of the subsequent jobs Dad pursued remain a mystery to me, as we were left behind in Panama under the care of our grandmother. With his dreams temporarily deferred, Dad ventured into unknown territory in pursuit of other employment opportunities. His journey led him down different paths as he sought to provide for our family, navigating the challenges and uncertainties that lay ahead.

All we knew from this point on was gleaned from the letters we received. Mom and Dad had departed for the United States to prepare the way for us to join them. Left behind, my brothers and I found ourselves under the care of our grandmother while my two sisters sought refuge with friends. In those days, the lack of a car in both households meant that the boys and girls rarely had the chance to see each other. Despite the physical distance, we found solace in knowing we were surrounded by family. My grandmother's home was always bustling with activity. In addition to our own family, she also housed my aunt, her husband, and my three male cousins. And then there was her son, my uncle, who was considerably older than the rest of us and often ventured down a deviant path.

Life in this new setting was different from Cocoli, but we made the best of it. Times were simpler then, and young kids like us were allowed to roam and play outside without constant supervision. It was a world where scraped knees and minor injuries were a regular part of childhood. I vividly recall the day my younger brother decided to scale a lemon tree in the backyard. Lemon trees, as we soon discovered, were adorned with sharp thorns. Inevitably, one of those thorns punctured my brother's head, and blood trickled down his face. Helpless, I could only offer words of advice, urging him to yank it out. But fear held him captive, and I hurried to seek the aid of our grandmother. With her gentle touch, she extracted the thorn and tended to his wound. Laughter replaced the initial shock as we realized the absurdity of the situation.

Life with my grandmother came with its unique set of responsibilities. She maintained a flock of chickens, and it became my duty to catch them and ring their necks. One by one, I would chase the chickens around the yard until I managed to grasp one firmly in my hands. It was a task that required both skill and courage. The ritual of ringing their necks was initially unsettling, but it was a necessary part of survival. However, fate took a peculiar turn when I acquired a little chick of my own. I had purchased it for a mere nickel, and from that moment, it became my cherished companion. I nurtured it, fed it, and watched it grow. The bond between us was undeniable. So, when the time came for my grandmother to ask me to retrieve my chicken for dinner, I couldn't bear the thought of parting with my beloved feathered friend. With tears streaming down my face, I adamantly refused to carry out the task. Sensing my distress, my grandmother relented and decided we would eat another chicken instead. A few days later, tragedy struck. My little chicken had gone missing, and to my dismay, we discovered that the neighbor's dog had killed and devoured it. With her wisdom, my grandmother offered a gentle reminder, "Even if we hadn't eaten it, it would have met the same fate."

As days turned into weeks and weeks into months, our yearning to reunite with our parents grew stronger. The letters they sent provided glimpses of their new life in the United States, but they were never enough. We longed to embrace them, to feel their presence once again. The absence of their physical presence left an emptiness in our hearts, and we relied on the memories we held dear to sustain us. Despite the challenges we faced, our spirits remained resilient. We found solace in our surroundings' familiarity and our extended family's support.

As time passed, the day of our long-awaited reunion finally arrived. Mom and Dad had paved the way, and now it was our turn to embark on the journey that would reunite us as a family. The challenges we had endured forged an unbreakable bond that would withstand the test of time. With eager hearts and joyful anticipation, we bid farewell to our grandmother and the place we had come to call home. The memories we had created would forever hold a special place in our hearts, serving as a testament to the strength of family and the resilience of the human spirit.

Gleaned - To obtain information or knowledge from various sources.

Deviant - Departing from usual or accepted standards, especially in behavior.

Solace - Comfort or relief in times of distress or sadness.

Bustling - Full of energetic and noisy activity.

Adorned - Decorated or embellished with something attractive or beautiful.

Nurture - To care for and encourage the growth or development of someone or something.

Grasp - To seize or hold firmly.

Ritual - A set of actions or ceremonies performed in a prescribed manner.

Parting - The action of leaving someone or something.

Adamantly - In a determined and unyielding manner.

Yearning - A strong feeling of intense longing or desire.

Resilient - Able to withstand or recover quickly from difficult conditions.

Emptiness - A feeling of loneliness or sadness due to the absence of something or someone.

Pillar - A person or thing regarded as a chief supporter or stabilizing force.

Endure - To suffer patiently or persistently; to withstand hardships.

Moving to the US

The day finally arrived, brimming with anticipation and a touch of nervousness, as my six siblings and I embarked on our first-ever flight to the United States. It had been two long years since my parents made the courageous decision to leave our home in Panama, and now, at the age of 10, I was eager to embrace this new chapter in our lives. As we bid farewell to our grandmother, aunt, and three cousins at the terminal, excitement coursed through our veins. We were embarking on an adventure, accompanied only by our youthful spirits and a sense of wanderlust.

Seated on the plane, I had envisioned myself gazing out of a window, marveling at the world from above. However, fate had placed me in the middle aisle, separated from my siblings. Despite the initial disappointment, I remained determined to make the most of this experience. The two-hour flight felt like an eternity, as I eagerly awaited the moment when we would touch down in Miami, Florida, and reunite with our beloved mom and, of course, Dad.

Having spent three years in Panama with military friends who spoke so much about the United States, we harbored a sense of familiarity as we came to this land of opportunities. Our youthful minds painted a picture of a place devoid of poverty, where everyone drove luxurious cars and resided in magnificent houses. We had heard our family friends complain about roaches, mice, and rats in Panama, and we naively assumed that such pests were nonexistent in this new country. Moreover, Dad's letters from the US hinted at a life filled with promise—he mentioned purchasing a car and securing a place for us to call home. While the airplane ride was thrilling, it was the prospect of owning our own car that truly excited me. As we prepared for landing, I was oblivious to the discomfort my inner ear would soon encounter, with no familiar adult to turn to for solace.

Finally, we arrived in the United States, our hearts pounding with excitement. After completing the necessary legal procedures, we were overjoyed at the prospect of reuniting with Mom. Words flowed freely from my younger brother's and older sister's lips as they animatedly recounted the details of our journey, leaving me content to silently observe the scene unfold. As we approached the parking lot, a surge of anticipation gripped me, envisioning a sleek, black, and elegant car waiting to whisk us away. However, reality had a different plan in store for us. The car before us was not ours. One by one, we passed by other vehicles, each one falling short of the image I had conjured in my mind. And then, we found ourselves face to face with the least appealing car in the lot—an unpleasant shade of puke yellow.

To compound matters, the car could only accommodate six passengers, leaving our family of nine in a state of bewilderment. It is important to note that my disappointment did not stem from the car itself but rather from the stark contrast between my imagination and the reality before me. Coming from a background of poverty, my parents had managed to carve out a comfortable life through their service in the army back in Panama. However, the car we now found ourselves with appeared worse than what we had left behind. At that moment, a flicker of doubt crept into my mind, questioning whether this journey was leading us towards a better life or a worse one.

Determined to hold onto hope, I eagerly turned my attention to our new house as we journeyed through the sights of Miami. The sprawling highways, where drivers obeyed traffic signs, and the pristine cleanliness of the streets captivated my young eyes. Our expectations soared as we arrived at our new abode, but reality struck once again. The small house that awaited us was painted in a yellow mustard hue, mirroring the less-than-appealing color of our puke-yellow car. Exhaustion washed over us, mingled with a tinge of disillusionment. We were all acutely aware of the tremendous effort and sacrifices our parents had made to bring us here. Stepping into the house, we discovered that it consisted of a single bedroom with a walk-in closet. Though an improvement from our previous living conditions in Rio Abajo, it did not quite match the standards we had grown accustomed to in Parke Lefebvre. Nevertheless, we held onto the belief that being together as a family was paramount and that brighter days lay ahead. With two more months until school began, we clung to the hope that our new life in the United States would gradually unfold.

The following morning, I awoke with a renewed sense of optimism, eager to explore our surroundings. I raced outside and beheld a mango tree standing tall near our fence line. It was a sight that filled me with a surge of hope and familiarity. A few mangoes had already fallen to the ground, beckoning me to savor their sweet succulence. Yet, as I hurried towards the tree, thorns unexpectedly pierced my foot. These painful intruders were known as sand spurs, a reminder that even in this new land, challenges and discomforts persisted. In Panama, they would merely cling to our clothes, but here, they inflicted physical pain when stepped on. Accustomed to the freedom of walking barefoot, it would take several months before I learned to don shoes before venturing outside, protecting myself from these prickly adversaries.

Vocabulary Words:

Disparity: Differences or contrasts, especially in relation to culture, background, or circumstances.

Nervousness: A feeling of unease or apprehension.

Anticipation: Excited expectation or eagerness for something to happen.

Predicament: A difficult or challenging situation.

Solace: Comfort or relief from sadness, loneliness, or distress.

Disillusioned: Disappointed or disenchanted, having lost faith or trust in something.

Resourcefulness: The ability to find clever and creative ways to use materials or solve problems.

Familiarity: A feeling of being acquainted with something or someone.

Imagination: The ability to create mental images or ideas.

Pristine: Clean, fresh, and in perfect condition

A Year of Wonders in the United States: Cockroach Strikes Back

My first year in the United States was nothing short of extraordinary. We arrived during the scorching summer months of July, and the moment we set foot on American soil, we were welcomed by an abundance of peculiar creatures that seemed to thrive in this new land. One creature, in particular, caught our attention with its alarming appearance, as if it had come straight out of a horror movie. The lubber grasshopper, adorned in hues of gold and orange, was accompanied by a smaller variant, black and red, and we couldn't help but be intrigued by their menacing size.

In our homeland of Panama, we were accustomed to playing with grasshoppers, but the lubber grasshoppers in the United States were different. Their legs were equipped with tiny barbs that stung when touched, making us wary of handling them. However, our curiosity overpowered our apprehension, and we tried to approach them with caution. To our surprise, the lubber grasshoppers emitted a white foam-like substance from their mouths, containing partially digested plants and digestive enzymes. It was a startling revelation, but we soon learned that this foam was their way of defending against potential predators. These fascinating insects were not only large and formidable but also protected themselves with an ingenious mechanism. We continued to play with them throwing them on each other while avoiding falling to the ground since we found ourselves in a constant battle with the aggressive plants that inhabited the sandy yard of our new home. Falling on the ground left us covered in tiny barbs, a new experience that we had to navigate carefully.

Within the confines of our tiny house, we discovered a rather peculiar and endearing guest, the Miami Gecko. The gecko, with its striking appearance and quick movements, initially seemed intimidating. Yet, to our delight, we realized that this little reptile was a friendly presence in our abode. The Miami Gecko proved to be beneficial, as it preyed on other unwanted pests that lurked within our walls. It became our unassuming housemate, a creature we learned to appreciate and befriend.

However, not all our newfound companions were as amiable as the Miami Gecko. Among the pests that we encountered, the American cockroach stood out as a giant in comparison to the German cockroaches we were familiar with from Panama. These resilient insects were astonishingly ancient, having been around since the time of dinosaurs! Their ability to survive without food for almost a month, and without water for about two weeks, was awe-inspiring. Even more incredible was the fact that a cockroach could live for up to one week without its head! Additionally, they could hold their breath for an impressive 40 minutes, and some female cockroaches only mated once in their lifetimes, remaining pregnant indefinitely. This was truly a species that had mastered the art of survival.

One memorable encounter with the American cockroach left a lasting impression on our family. Spotting one of these giants scurrying across the floor, my mother decided to take matters into her own hands. She hurried to the store, returning with a can of roach spray, determined to eliminate the intruder. Little did she know that American roaches had a penchant for defiance. As she unleashed the spray, the cockroach seemingly took offense and went airborne, charging straight at her. Laughter ensued, and we couldn't help but marvel at the tenacity of these resilient creatures. She exclaimed that American roaches fight back.

But it wasn't just the creatures within our home that captivated us; the surrounding environment held wonders of its own. The bullfrogs of Miami were an extraordinary sight to behold. These colossal amphibians, with their bodies reaching up to 8 inches in length, were unlike any frogs we had encountered in Panama. Enthralled by their size, we decided to collect as many as we could fill in a box, oblivious to the potential dangers, but this is a story in another chapter.

As we soon discovered, the Everglades bullfrog secreted a poison from glands on the side of its face. While harmless to humans, the poison was toxic to animals that dared to prey on these magnificent amphibians. It was a valuable lesson in appreciating nature's intricate balance and the importance of respecting the boundaries of wild creatures.

Throughout our first year in the United States, we encountered numerous fascinating and occasionally challenging creatures. Rats, alligators, and water moccasins were among the creatures we faced in later adventures, each with its own tale to tell. But for now, we reveled in the wonders of the American landscape, embracing every encounter with curiosity and excitement.

As time went on, we adapted to our new home, learning to appreciate the diversity and resilience of the creatures that shared this land with us. Our first year in the United States became a remarkable journey of exploration and discovery, filled with countless stories that would stay with us for a lifetime. Our encounters with the unique and sometimes mysterious creatures of America shaped our understanding of the natural world and instilled a profound sense of wonder that would endure for years to come.

Vocabulary Words:

Scorching - extremely hot or burning.

Ingenious - clever, inventive, and resourceful.

Apprehension - anxiety or fear about future events.

Endearing - inspiring affection or fondness.

Peculiar - strange or unusual; distinct from others.

Resilient - able to withstand or recover quickly from difficult conditions.

Awe-inspiring - evoking a feeling of amazement and reverence.

Tenacity - the quality of holding fast, persistence, and determination.

Captivated - greatly interested or fascinated.

Intruder - a person or thing that enters a place without permission or welcome.

Enthralled - capturing one's complete attention; mesmerized.

Obvious - easily seen, recognized, or understood; clear.

Intertwined - connected or linked closely together.

Wilderness - a wild and natural area undisturbed by human activity.

Endure - to continue to exist or last; to bear or withstand.

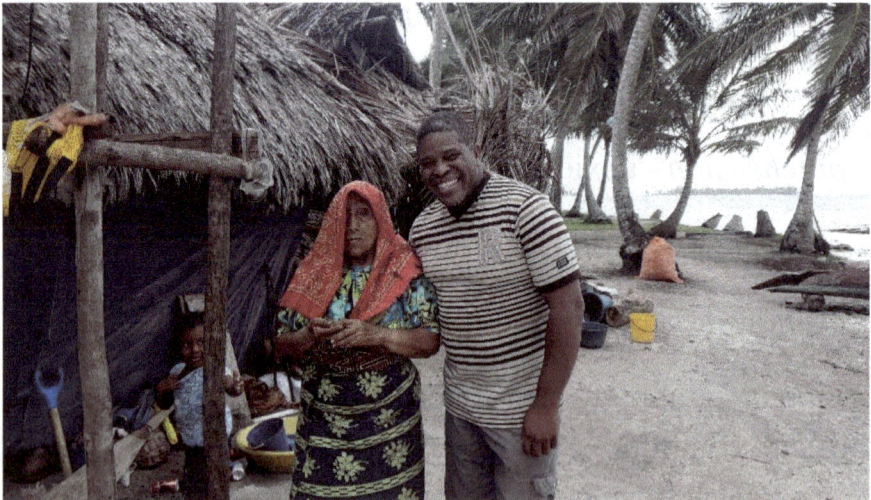

www.ingramcontent.com/pod-product-compliance
Lightning Source LLC
Chambersburg PA
CBHW070845300326
41935CB00039B/1535